Layered Curriculum® Workbook
2nd edition

A workbook for designing Layered Curriculum® teaching units. This workbook is a companion to *Layered Curriculum: The practical solution for teachers with more than one student in their classroom, 2nd edition* (Brains.org)

ISBN 978-1-929358-14-4

Additional copies of this workbook as well as all books by Kathie F Nunley
are available at:
Brains.org & Help4Teachers.com

For further information and sample Layered Curriculum® units visit:
http://Help4Teachers.com

Published 2007
BRAINS.ORG
Amherst, NH

Cover Design by Micheal R Eudy
Eudy Animation: Dallas, Texas

Layered Curriculum® is a registered trademark created and owned by
Dr Kathie F Nunley. Inquire for usage guidelines.

Printed in the USA by Morris Publishing
Kearney, NE 68847

Foreword

Most teachers recognize that survival in today's mixed-ability classrooms means moving away from the traditional, stand-and-deliver, teacher-centered approach. Unfortunately many of us received limited training in how to run a differentiated, student-centered classroom. Layered Curriculum® provides a simple, easy to manage solution strategy.

Originally designed for the secondary classroom, Layered Curriculum® is now one of the most popular teaching methods in classrooms around the globe ranging from kindergarten to graduate school. Its popularity can be attributed to its ease of implementation, tremendous latitude in modification to fit individual teaching style, school, district and population requirements, and strong emphasis on student accountability.

This workbook is designed as an accompaniment to the text, *Layered Curriculum: The practical solution for teachers with more than one student in their classroom.* This updated version is aligned with the 2nd edition of the text and includes expanded ideas, formats and problems specific to certain disciplines, such as math. Refer to the main text for frequently asked questions, implementation strategies and additional sample units.

In this workbook you will find examples for each of the activities.

> **Examples** of the activities are included in this type of text box and will generally be found on the LEFT side pages of the workbook.

> Activities **for you to complete** for your specific classroom are included in this type of box and will generally be found on the RIGHT side pages of the workbook.

Refer to the website (Help4Teachers.com) for additional support, hundreds of sample units, teaching tips, and articles. If you have further questions as you work through design and implementation, please visit the discussion board at the website.
Best of luck on your voyage.

-Kathie

Table of Contents

Evaluating Your Layered Curriculum® Unit AFTER It's Over

Where do I Start? : **Warm-up Exercises**

As the text reminds you, start slow and with your current teaching style and strategy. While you may be anxious to "jump right in" to a full-blown Layered Curriculum® unit, most teachers find success by starting with what they do currently, then adding each of the **3 keys to Layered Curriculum®** one, by one.

- Student Choice
- Encourage Higher Level Thinking
- Hold Students Accountable for Actual Learning

Details on each of these can be found on page 50-51 in the text. This first workbook chapter will help you brainstorm ideas for each of these 3 keys.

We'll start by simply thinking about adding choice to our current objectives and teaching schemata. It's easy and fun to add some variation and let students choose one or two of your assignment choices. You can continue adding choices as you and your students find your "choice comfort level."

After we add choice, we'll look at demarcating our grading scheme to encourage higher level thinking. Later in this workbook we'll address grade book issues and modifications for various grading systems.

Lastly, we'll need to think about how to hold our students accountable for learning. The text discusses oral defense and other accountability options. We'll need to find a way to work this key into our existing school and teaching system.

KEY #1: Choice

Example: I'm teaching a unit on Bacteria in high school biology. Some of my unit objectives are:

> 1. Students will be able to distinguish a <u>Bacteria Cell</u> from a <u>True Cell.</u>
> 2. Students will be able to recognize and label 3 main shapes and 3 main arrangements of bacteria cells.
> 3. Students will understand the terms <u>phototrophic</u>, <u>chemotrophic</u>, <u>thermophilic</u>, <u>halophilic</u>, and <u>archaebacteria</u>.

In a traditional high school classroom I might lecture briefly on these topics, assign students to read the text and perhaps answer book questions or complete a publisher worksheet. If I were just beginning Layered Curriculum® I might want to start by keeping my daily lectures on each of the topics, but add some choice in how the students achieve these 3 objectives in addition to the text and publisher worksheets.

> 1. Students will be able to distinguish a Bacteria Cell from a True Cell.
> Activity Choices:
> a. lecture
> b. text reading
> c. computer / internet search- annotated search
> d. bulletin board display
>
> 2. Students will be able to recognize and label 3 main shapes and 3 main arrangements of bacteria cells.
> Activity Choices:
> a. lecture
> b. text reading
> c. design a pamphlet
> d. clay models
>
> 3. Students will understand the terms phototrophic, chemotrophic, thermophilic, halophilic, and archaebacteria.
> Activity Choices:
> a. flashcards
> b. partner quizzes
> c. cartoon illustrations

Now you try this idea with a unit you currently teach.

List 3 student objectives you have established (or been assigned) on a current unit of study:

1.

2.

3.

For each of the 3 objectives above, list 3 assignment choices that may help students learn that objective.

Objective #1:
a.

b.

c.

Objective #2:
a.

b.

c.

Objective # 3:
a.

b.

c.

Key #2: Encourage Higher Level Thinking

This second Layered Curriculum® key refers to arbitrarily setting 2 or 3 boundaries which become the layers in your grading system. In order to pass into the next layer, students must think more complexly. Layered Curriculum® starts students thinking in concrete terms, adding to their bank of knowledge (The C layer). Then we move students into an application or manipulation layer where they are required to attach new knowledge to prior knowledge (The B layer). Finally students are brought into the more complex thinking, analytical evaluation of real-world situations (The A layer).

The layers are named after the traditional grading system of A, B, C, D, F. A Layered Curriculum® teacher though does not need to feel locked into this grade system or excluded from the model if his or her school uses a different scheme.

Here are 2 examples of using Layered Curriculum® with various teacher grading schemes.

I use an A, B, C, D F scheme at my school.

> Students must listen to my lectures each day and complete 3 moderate (10 point) assignments at a competent level in order to earn a C.
> Students must complete one of my lab projects (in addition to C layer work) to a competent level to earn a B.
> Students must complete the above plus do one A layer question to a competent level to earn an A.

I use number grades at my school. (Percentile marks, eg: 78, 83, 98)

> Students can earn up to 73 points on bottom C layer work.
> In order to move above 73 the students must complete a B layer assignment.
> In order to move above 92 points, my students must complete an A layer assignment

You will have an opportunity to work out your grading schema later in this workbook, but you may want to start thinking about your personal expectations for your teaching area.

Notes and Ideas about my Grading Scheme.
Include here what your school or district requires for reporting grades. Include things such as required percentages that must come from exams, homework, etc. You will use this information later when you actually build your grading scale.

Key 3: Increase Student Accountability

The text covers in detail the main type of accountability used in Layered Curriculum®, oral defense. Most teachers find this a bit overwhelming in the beginning, so don't try to grade every assignment by every student, every day, using oral defense. Consider using some of the other ideas mentioned in the text such as small homework discussion or quick spot quizzes.

Ideas for increasing accountability in my classroom

Oral Defense (as much as I can find time for)

Small Group Quizzes on the Overhead

Peer Tutors

Homework Discussion Groups

Key 3: Increase Student Accountability

Ideas for increasing accountability in my classroom

Building Our First Unit

Now that you've had some time to brainstorm a bit, let's get started designing your first unit of Layered Curriculum®. We'll start with a daily method of Layered Curriculum® to help you and your students become accustomed to the format and the idea of making choices. I always suggest you start with at least one daily unit so that students can understand and experience success in all 3 layers.   Then we'll move into the traditional, full-blown Layered Curriculum® format for those of you who would like to try that.

Daily Method of Layered Curriculum®

- One of the best ways to begin
- Limits student's choices to just 2 or 3 per day
- Walks all students through <u>all 3 layers</u> at teacher-set pace

Traditional Method of Layered Curriculum®

- Allows students more choices each day
- Lays out the entire unit together
- Allows students to move through the layers at their own pace

Building a "Daily Method" Layered Curriculum® Unit
(High School Biology)

Step One: Decide on a topic for the unit.

My Unit Topic will be:

Plants

Step Two. Decide on the duration of the unit.

My Unit will last:

7 days

Step Three: Establish a central/key topic for each day.

Key Daily Topics for this Unit:

day 1: Evolution of the Plant Kingdom
day 2: Reproduction in gymnosperms.
day 3: Reproduction in angiosperms.
day 4: Stem, leaves, tissues.
day 5: Seed dispersal / pollination.
day 6 & 7 will be for B and A layer.

Building a "Daily Method" Layered Curriculum® Unit

Step One: Decide on a topic for the unit

A unit can be any length, though I would not recommend much more than what you would normally put in a week's lesson plan. Units may be based on a textbook chapter, theme, or important skill, e.g.: "Plants," "The French - Indian War", "Nouns," "Double Digit Addition," "Forces", etc.

If a chapter or topic is exceptionally large, consider dividing it into two or more units. (For example, in general biology, I usually divide "Genetics" into two units, Mendelian, and Non-Mendelian, whereas the Animal Kingdom is divided into 5 units.)   In the beginning, small is better than large.

My Unit Topic will be:_____

Step Two. Decide on the duration of the unit.
How many days will the unit last? Again, my suggestion is to go small, rather than large. A week is a popular length, but feel free to try short units of two or three days. Two weeks would be the absolute maximum I would suggest. Younger children do better with shorter units. Kindergarten/First grade may want to design units that are started and finished the same day.

My Unit will last: _____ days.

Step Three: Establish a central/key topic for each day.
This would be a topic that you plan to lecture on, or give some whole class instruction. If you are using a textbook chapter for your unit, these topics may be gleaned from the subheading or key ideas of the chapter. Even if your unit will only last one day, you may want to list 2 or 3 key topics for the lesson.

Key Daily Topics for this Unit:

_____   _____   _____

_____   _____   _____

Day 1 Topic:

Evolution of the Plant Kingdom.

- 15 min video on evolution of plant kingdom
- computer program on early seedless vascular plants
- end of chapter questions from text #1 – 8
- worksheet from text chapter 16

Day 2 Topic:

Reproduction in Gymnosperms

- poster of pine tree life cycle
- computer program on reproduction in cone plants
- worksheet – choose any 2
  video: Private Lives of Plants, part 1

Step Four: Building the C layer.

Here's where it gets fun. This section is a great place to work with a colleague. Take each of your topics from step three, one at a time, and list 2 - 4 assignment choices for each. Try to be creative. You want to hit all the learning styles that may be represented in your classroom. Even if all your students are visual/auditory learners, try to avoid listing 4 different worksheets. For ideas, refer to pages 27-31 in the text *Layered Curriculum, 2nd edition* for suggested C layer activities or the appendix in this workbook.

Day One Topic:_____

- 1.

- 2.

- 3.

- 4.

Day Two Topic:_____

- 1.

- 2.

- 3.

- 4.

(Continued on next page)

Day 3 Topic:

Reproduction in angiosperms.

- vocabulary flash cards - from entire chapter
- poster / drawing showing flowering plant life cycle
- worksheet - choose any 2 from packet
- audio listening station, using text

Day 4 Topic:

Stems/leaves/tissues

- worksheets - choose any two (with text reading)
- cross-section diagrams of dicot/monocot/woody stem
- leaf rubbings - venation identification (from home)
- video - Private Life of Plants, continued from day 2.

Day 5 Topic:

Seed dispersal/pollination

- complete the seed lab with worksheet
- computer program on seed dispersal
- textbook questions # 9-16.

Continuing the C layer

Day Three Topic:_____

-     1.

-     2.

-     3.

-     4.

Day Four Topic:_____

-     1.

-     2.

-     3.

-     4.

Day Five Topic:_____

-     1.

-     2.

-     3.

-     4.

The activities you have just written in step four make up your *C layer*. As we'll see later, you can offer them to your students just as you wrote them, divided into days (a daily method) or you can put them all together in a traditional Layered Curriculum® format as we'll build later in this workbook

B layer (Student Labs)

1. Flower dissection (find a perfect and an imperfect flower, dissect, mount individual parts as listed on board). Be able to identify.

2. Scavenger Hunt - students will find the items from my list in nature. Can be done outside in the school yard during class or as homework assignment.

3. Does Miracle-gro work? Design and implement a lab to prove it. (Due within 2 weeks)

Step Five: Build your B layer

Brainstorm 2- 4 *B layer* application/problem solving activities for the unit. If possible, keep the assignments unusual, especially at the beginning of the year when students may need some encouragement to move into this layer.

This layer is designed to give students an opportunity to apply some of the basic skills they learned in the *C layer*. If they learned vocabulary, have them use it. If they learned kitchen techniques, have them prepare a food dish. If they learned word processing skills, have them demonstrate their use in an assignment for perhaps one of their other classes. If they learned about a period of history, have them find places today that either repeat the same issues or where communities have behaved differently because of the lessons learned from those earlier periods. If they are learning what goes in an English theme, have them write the paper. If they are learning about physics laws have them build demonstrations of those laws. If they are learning about bacteria, have them design a lab to vary its growth. For details on the B layer, refer to Chapter Five in the text *Layered Curriculum, 2nd ed.*

1.

2.

3.

4.

A Layer Questions

1. Are bio-engineered plants safe to eat?

2. Can we prevent bio-terrorism threats to our farms?

3. Is Ethanol-85 a good solution to our gas shortage? What is its impact on farmers, pro & con?

Step Six: Build your A layer

Here you want to brainstorm 2- 4 *A layer* critical thinking/real world issues for the unit. This layer will help train students to be contributing member of our society (ie: voters). This is the most elaborate layer only in terms of the complexity of thought needed to complete it. You want students to understand that the real world doesn't always come with a right or wrong answer. Sometimes decisions are made which involve personal values and beliefs in addition to hard scientific evidence.

Whenever possible try to link this section to current news issues. To complete the assignment, the student will choose one of the questions, find 3 or 4 opinions on the issue, then form their own opinions after bouncing the ideas gathered around with their own beliefs, thoughts and knowledge. Additional information is available in Chapter 6 of *Layered Curriculum, 2nd ed.* There are also suggested *A layer* questions in the appendix of this workbook along with a sample *A Layer Assignment Form.*

1.

2.

3.

4.

Presenting Sample Plant Unit in a "Daily Method" Layered Curriculum Form

----

Name_____ Due Date:_____ Your Score _____/100 max

Unit 3: Plants
(assignments with an "*" are REQUIRED and will be done as a class)

Day One: Do Two
*1. Listen to the lecture, take notes **(5pts)**
2. Watch the video on evolution of plant kingdom - write 5 things learned.**(10pts)**
3. Work the computer program on early seedless vascular plants. **(10pts)**
4. Read the HBJ text Chapter on plants. Be able to answer #1-8 pg. 342. **(15pts)**

Day Two: Do Two
*1. Listen to the lecture, take notes **(5pts)**
2. Choose one or two blue worksheet from text chapter 16. **(5pts each)**
3. Design a poster of pine tree life cycle. **(15pts)**
4. Work the computer program on reproduction in cone plants. **(10pts)**
5. Choose one or two green worksheets. **(5pts each)**

Day Three: Do One or Two
*1. Listen to the lecture, take notes **(5pts)**
2. Watch the video: Private Life of Plants - part one. **(5pts)**
3. Complete the video worksheet packet from "Private Life of Plants." **(10pts)**
4. Make vocabulary flashcards from board list. Learn them. **(10pts)**
5. Design a poster/drawing showing flowering plant life cycle **(15pts)**
6. Choose one or two yellow worksheets.**(5pts each)**
7. Listen to the audio listening station - using HOLT textbook in Spanish. **(10pts)**

Day Four: Do Two or Three
*1. Listen to the lecture, take notes **(5pts)**
2. Read the Morris Text Chapter 12 - Do the worksheet.**(10pts)**
3. Make 3 cross-section diagrams of dicot/monocot/woody stem. **(5pts)**
4. Find 10 leaves showing 3 different venations. Make rubbings. Label. **(5pts)**

Day Five: Do Two or Three
*1. Listen to the lecture, take notes **(5pts)**
2. Do the seed lab (#12). Complete the lab worksheet. **(10pts)**
3. Work the computer program on seed dispersal. **(10pts)**
4. Using the HBJ text, be able to answer questions # 9-16 on pg. 343.**(15pts)**

(Continued)

(Plant Unit continued)

Day Six: B layer work: Choose one of the following labs. **15 points**

1. Flower dissection. Find a perfect and imperfect flower, dissect and mount individual parts as listed on board. Be able to identify all the parts.

2. Scavenger Hunt - using the items on the scavenger list, find evidence of these in nature. You may use the school grounds today or do this as homework if you need the day to finish C layer activities.

3. Does Miracle-gro work? Design and implement a lab to prove it. I need your question, hypothesis and written description of your procedure at this end of this day. You also need to have started your lab. The data and conclusion are due in 2 weeks.

Day Seven: A layer work. Using an A layer assignment sheet, **complete one** of the following issue evaluations. We will meet in the media center as a class on this day.
20 points

1. Are bio-engineered plants safe to eat?
2. Can we prevent bio-terrorism threats to our farms?
3. Is Ethanol-85 a good solution to our gas shortage? What is its impact on farmers, pro & con?

Grade Scale: 41-55=D   56-70=C   71-85=B   86+=A

Notes:

This format is most appropriate when introducing Layered Curriculum to students. It provides a lot more structure, but still gives some options. It may be the way you would like to design your first couple of units until both you and your students have a good feel for student-centered instruction.

In this format, I have basically left assignments just as I originally designed them, separated by daily lecture topic. Notice that some assignments can be required (such as the lecture).

Another option I've used, is to make this a 5 day unit and simply integrate the *B layer* activity into the unit on Day 4 and the A layer into Day 5:

Day Four: **Do Two or Three**
*1. Listen to the lecture, take notes **(5pts)**
2. Read the Morris Text Chapter 12 - Do the worksheet.**(10pts)**
3. Make 3 cross-section diagrams of dicot/monocot/woody stem. **(5pts)**
4. Find 10 leaves showing 3 different venations. Make rubbings. Label. **(5pts)**
*5. Does Miracle-gro work? Design and implement a lab to prove it. **(15pts.)**

Day Five: **Do Two or Three**
*1. Listen to the lecture, take notes **(5pts)**
2. Do the seed lab (#12). Complete the lab worksheet. **(10pts)**
3. Work the computer program on seed dispersal. **(10pts)**
4. Using the HBJ text, be able to answer questions # 9-16 on pg. 343.**(15pts)**
*5. Are pesticides on crops worth the risk? (Use A level form for this) **(20 pts)**

In this variation, we will do a lab, of my choosing, so that I can provide some direct instruction on how to do a lab, how to clean up, and how to present data. This particular lab (sprouting a seed) would obviously take longer than a day to get results. In situations like this, I will still collect the unit sheets on day 5, but will go back days or weeks later to add in their lab points as it becomes complete.

You'll see that the *A layer* activity has been integrated into the unit on Day 5. We will also do this activity, of my choosing, together. For the first *A layer* activity, opinions may be gathered orally, from classmates. Due to time constraints, I might have them gather the opinions in class, but write their analysis as homework.

This type of daily method is used with populations who need lots of structure or are just starting Layered Curriculum®. It still provides some choice, but offers assignments in smaller packets or chunks so that the format of the class looks a little more traditional. Something will be turned in at the end of each class period. Students can complete some assignments as homework or finish them the next day if necessary.

I could also add a 50 point formal exam to the end of this unit making the entire unit worth 150 points rather than 100 points.

Creating "Traditional" Layered Curriculum® Units

While I always encourage teachers to begin with at least one or two units of "Daily Method" Layered Curriculum®, you may want to move into the more traditional method as you and your students get comfortable with choice and confident in setting deadlines.

The traditional Layered Curriculum® gives students more choice in the order in which they do assignments. You may allow students to work on any of the C layer assignments on any day, or you may even decide that they can start A layer or B layer activities before finishing the C layer. This traditional approach allows the most student choice.

Here is the exact same Plant unit offered in a traditional form:

Traditional Layered Curriculum® Format
Plant Unit

Name_____   Due Date:_____

Unit Three: Plants   Maximum 100 points

C layer: Maximum 65 points in this Section.
1. Listen to the lecture, take notes **(5pts/ day)**   1   2   3   4   5
2. Watch the video on evolution of plant kingdom - write 5 things learned. **(10pts)**
3. Work the computer program on early seedless vascular plants. **(10pts)**
4. Read the HBJ text Chapter on plants. Be able to answer #1-8 pg. 342. **(15pts)**
5. Choose one or two blue worksheet from text chapter 16. **(5pts each)**
6. Design a poster of pine tree life cycle. **(15pts)**
7. Work the computer program on reproduction in cone plants. **(10pts)**
8. Choose one or two green worksheets. **(5pts each)**
9. Watch the video: Private Life of Plants - part one. **(5pts)**
10 .Make vocabulary flashcards from board list. Learn them. **(10pts)**
11. Design a poster/drawing showing flowering plant life cycle **(15pts)**
12. Choose one or two yellow worksheets.**(5pts each)**
13. Listen to the audio listening station - using HOLT textbook in Spanish.**(10pts)**
14. Read the Morris Text Chapter 12 - Do the worksheet.**(10pts)**
15. Make 3 cross-section diagrams of dicot/monocot/woody stem. **(5pts)**
16. Find 10 leaves showing 3 different venations, make rubbings. Label.**(5pts)**
17. Watch the video - Private Life of Plants, continued from day 2. **(5pts)**
18. Complete the video worksheet packet from "Private Life of Plants."**(10pts)**
19. Do the seed lab (#12). Complete the lab worksheet. **(10pts)**
20. Work the computer program on seed dispersal. **(10pts)**
21. Using the HBJ text, be able to answer questions # 9-16 on pg.343.**(15pts)**

B layer - choose one ONLY. 15 points.

1. Flower dissection (bring in a perfect and an imperfect flower, dissect, mount individual parts as listed on board.) Be able to identify.
2. Scavenger Hunt - see list on board. (use an outside pass)
3. Does Miracle-gro work? Design and implement a lab to prove it.

A Layer - choose one ONLY 20 points. (Use A layer assignment form)
1. Are bio-engineered plants safe to eat?
2. Can we prevent bio-terrorism threats to our farms?
3. Is Ethanol-85 a good solution to our gas shortage?

Grade Scale: 41-55=D   56-70=C   71-85=B   86+=A

Notes:

This format is the traditional way Layered Curriculum® is done. The *C layer* assignments are offered together in one layer. Students are free to choose from a much wider range of assignments especially in the *B* and *A layers*. This particular unit has very little "whole class instruction" other than a daily lecture which is signed off by teacher initials over the top of the appropriate day number (1 2 3 4 5).

Notice in this unit, some assignments can be either blended or used as a stand-alone assignment depending on a student's ability or preference. For example, look at C layer assignments 9, 17, and 18. A student could watch the first half of the video, the first and second half, or watch it all and complete the worksheet. This makes an assignment much more accessible to a wider variety of students without stigmatizing any one. A student with limited reading/writing skills or limited English proficiency would be able to do one or two of these assignment, while other students may want to watch it and complete the worksheet that went with it.

Another important point: While a huge variety of learning styles is represented in the C layer, no particular learning style is so well represented that a student would be able to complete the entire layer in their preferred style. In other words, I can engage nearly all my students by offering assignments that suit their style, but once I have them engaged and they are experiencing some success, they will have to branch out from their comfort zone in order to complete the layer.

Modifications for a Variety of Subjects, Grade Levels and Specific Situations.

The following sections contain helpful ideas and samples for a variety of teaching situations. While Layered Curriculum® was originally designed for classes where the emphasis was put on "basic knowledge" (C layer), there are many situations where the B or even the A layer may be most important (eg: arts, P.E., technology, etc). You may be teaching a course where the curriculum must be presented in a "spiraling" format, or you may be teaching a subject where you need a lot of direct, whole class instruction. The following pages will help you design Layered Curriculum® for your specific situation.

Example of building a Layered Curriculum® unit when the B layer has the most emphasis.

My unit will last *5 days*

My unit topic is *Intro to Sewing*

C Layer topics

Day 1: Overview of the sewing machine (basic stitches, threading, setting the tension)
Day 2: Measuring, Fabric bias, pinning and sewing a seam and casing.

B Layer

The student will construct either a sports bag with drawstring, or a laundry bag with drawstring, or a drawstring decorative pillow case.

A Layer

The students will evaluate their project as well as sample projects brought in of various price.

Finished Unit - Middle School
(Family & Consumer Science, Sewing unit)

Day 1: Do each of the following: (5 points / each)

1. a. Watch the demonstration
or
1. b. Watch the video.

2. a. Label the worksheet on sewing machine.
or
2. b. Take the machine quiz and pass it.

3. Thread your sewing machine and adjust the tension in the machine and demonstrate proper tension on a scrap. (Can finish this tomorrow if needed)

Day 2: Do each of the following (5 points / each)

1. a. Watch the teacher demonstration
or
1. b. Watch the video demonstration.

2. Cut out your project, mark and pin the seams.

3. Pass a safety / procedures quiz

Day 3: (project worth 55 points on day 4)
Work on and complete your project

Day 4: Work on and complete your project.

Day 5: Evaluation Day:
1. Self evaluate your finished project with 2 classmates. Get input on what was good, what could be improved. 5 points
2. Your group needs to collect 3 items from the table, one from each price category. Discuss the construction on each and do ONE of the following:
a. Complete the evaluation sheet.
b. Plan a 30 second commercial touting the construction quality on the item you determine to have the best construction. Include comparison to the other products.
(10 points)

Your completed project is worth 55 points.
This unit is worth 100 points.

0 -30 F   31- 50 D,   51- 70 C   71- 89 B   90+A

Project-Based Layered Curriculum® units

Another option for Layered Curriculum® is a "project-based' unit. This type of unit is especially well suited for the social sciences and the hard sciences as the "project" is generally some type of display or fair (such as a history fair or science fair). The project itself is the B layer and the various sources and assignments that students can complete in order to put their project together become the C layer. Any type of evaluation extension of the work can be used in the A layer.

My Unit Topic will be: *the Holocaust*

My Unit will last: *5 days*

The project(s) will be:
- *history fair*
- *webpage*
- *news broadcast*

Example of a "Project Based" Layered Curriculum® unit

Unit Topic: **The Holocaust**

C Layer: - choose up to 5 of these for 10 points each. (Except 13*)

1. Watch one of the two videos on the Holocaust. Summarize in a paragraph the emotions the video elicited.
2. Research 10 websites on the topic. Make an annotated bibliography for the 10 sites.
3. Using one of our texts, read the chapter dealing with this topic and be prepared to answer the end of chapter questions.
4. Write a one page research report on one of the concentration camps.
5. Using recycled materials, make a model of one of the concentration camps.
6. Take a virtual tour of the national museum. Make a self-tour brochure that could be used by other visitors.
7. Using the novel from your English class, write a 150 word editorial arguing the value of the book for understanding the holocaust.
8. Imagine yourself as a holocaust survivor. Write a poem designed to share your feelings with the world.
9. Make a poster showing at least 10 charts / graphs illustrating the "numbers" statistics associated with the holocaust.
10. Find 3 newspaper articles from any major US newspaper during the holocaust which shows the US perspective during the event.
11. Read 2 interviews with holocaust survivors. Summarize what you feel are the 5 most significant details of the interview.
12. Make up to two 3-dimensional items for your history display.
*13. Listen to the class lecture on the topic. - 5 points / day.

This unit culminate in a **B layer project**:
(presentation of your learning **35 points**)

1. Participate in our "history fair" with a holocaust display. Your display can include a 3-panel project board or a 3 foot by 5 foot 3-D tabletop display. Include your projects and learning from the C layer.
2. Host a 15 minute "TV news story" on the Holocaust using video.
3. Build a Holocaust website. The site must be at least 4 pages deep.

A Layer: (15 points)

 Using the information you gleaned from at least 3 classmate's presentations, compare and contrast the Holocaust with either the current situation in Darfur or another international situation. Form an opinion on whether or not the US should play a humanitarian role for resolution.

Building a Layered Curriculum® unit based out of a text that "spirals" learning. (For upper elementary Math)

My Unit Topic will be: *(Saxon 54 lessons 71-73)*
remaining fraction, multiplying 3 factors, exponents, polygons

My Unit will last: *4 days*

Key Daily Topics for this Unit:

day 1. Lesson 71 remaining fractions

day 2. Lesson 72 multiplying 3 factors, exponents

day 3. Lesson 73, polygons

day 4. Review/assessment

Layered Curriculum® Workbook ©2007

Building the C layer.

day 1 Topic: *Remaining fractions*

getting the lesson - teacher quick lesson, read lesson from book, discuss lesson in small group

practice problems - small interactive poster, traditional, story form

review skills - group discussion with flash cards, practice

homework - review problems, peer tutor, going further

day 2 Topic: *Multiplying 3 factors, exponents*

getting the lesson - teacher quick lesson, read lesson from book, discuss lesson in small group

practice problems - small interactive poster, traditional, story form

review skills - group discussion with flashcards, practice

homework - review problems, peer tutor, going further

day 3 Topic: *Polygons*

getting the lesson - teacher quick lesson, read lesson from book, discuss lesson in small group

practice problems - collage, mobile, computer program

review skills - group discussion with flashcards, practice

homework - review problems, peer tutor, going further

Build your B layer

1. Design a house floor plan using polygons. Label.

2. Find 1/3 of our school (with groups using remaining fractions concept) sketch. Label polygons.

Build your A layer

1. Analyze the color percentages in a garden. How would you change it to fit a church, a gas station, the Olympic village.

2. Analyze a property tax statement. What percentages are spent on different community items. Does this need to be changed?

Presenting Spiraling (math) Unit in a Traditional Layered Curriculum Format. . .

Saxon 54 Math

Lesson 71 - 73
Name_____ Due Date_____

| 61- 70 = D | 71-80 = C | 81-90= B | 91+ = A |

C layer - no more than 80 points

1. Learn the new skill: Choose Two **5 pts/each**
a. Teacher quick lesson 71
b. Read pg. 242 alone
c. Discuss pg. 242 with partner

2. Practice the skill: Choose One **5 pts/each**
a. Make an interactive poster teaching one of # 1-6.
b. Answer/work # 1-6 on paper.
c. Draw a story for #3.

3. Review previous skills: Choose One **5 pts/each**
a. With a group of 3 other classmates, make flash cards of review #7-20. Do mental math discussion until everyone knows the skills.
b. Be able to complete any of the review questions. (Draw 2 cards).

4. Learn the new skill: Choose Two **5 pts/each**
a. Teacher quick lesson 72
b. Read pg. 245 alone
c. Discuss pg. 245 with partner

5. Practice the skill: Choose One **5 pts/each**
a. Make an interactive poster teaching one of # 1-11.
b. Answer/work # 1-11 on paper.
c. Draw a story for # 1 & 2.

6. Review previous skills: Choose One **5 pts/each**
a. With a group of 3 other classmates, make flash cards of review #12-25. Do mental math discussion until everyone knows the skills.
b. Be able to complete any of the review questions. (Draw 2 cards)..

7. Learn the new skill: Choose Two **5 pts/each**
a. Teacher quick lesson 73
b. Read pg. 248 alone
c. Discuss pg. 248 with partner

8. Practice the skill: Choose One **10 pts/each**
a. Make an mobile, or collage showing 13 different polygons. Label them.
b. Answer/work # 1-6 on paper.
c. Work the computer program.

(Continued. . .)

9. Review previous skills: Choose One **5 pts/each**
1. Pass the quiz
2. Work the review problem sheet.

Homework Options: (choose 3 - 1 due each day) - 5 pts./each
1. Practice sheet - fractions
2. Practice sheet - polygons
3. Practice sheet - review problems
4. Do an internet report on a mathematician
5. After school tutor session for 2/3 graders - math.
6. Complete Math Kitchen Lab #23.

B Level: Choose one - 10 points

1. Design a house floor plan involving 6 different polygons. Mark the scale.
Calculate the area of 3 rooms. Pose 3 questions about your house involving
fractions. Discuss it with me and 2 classmates.

2. With 2 classmates, estimate what would be 1/3 of our school. Sketch the
floor plan of that area. Label the polygons.

A Layer: Choose One - use an A layer assignment sheet - 10 points

1. Analyze the flower gardens in the magazines at the board. Choose one
and figure the approximate percentage of each color. How would you
recommend they change these percentages if the garden were in front of a
church? A gas station? The Olympic village?

2. Using a property tax statement (your own or one of my samples), analyze
the percentage of tax spent on different community items. Are these fair
percentages?

Notes:

Math, like many other subjects, often builds skill upon skill as the year or unit progresses. For this reason, it may be necessary for students to complete one skill before moving on to the next. In this unit, students are required to do something from each skill level, but they still have choice within the skill area.

The text book used for this unit (Saxon) has formatted each lesson into three parts, introduce a new skill, practice that skill, and review previous skills. This Layered Curriculum unit maintains that same format. Students choose something within each part.

Also note that two of the days look almost identical in the activities, only the topic has changed. Day three offers a little more variety as the topic of polygons lends itself well to hands-on projects and a computer program was available.

To run this unit, the teacher would introduce each of the three topics with a brief (10 minute) teacher "quick lesson" at the board. Students would then have time to read the book's presentation either individually or in groups, and the remainder of the class time would be on their practice and review assignments.

Day four is spent reviewing the new material and allowing time for students to complete their *B layer* assignments. Some students may have already started their *B* assignment if they had left-over time earlier in the unit. The *A layer* could either be done in or out of class, depending on the teacher's time constraints.

Another thing to note in this unit is that some assignments are specifically assigned as homework. This school has a policy that homework will be assigned. The homework is separated and put in the *C layer*, but choice is given here as well.

Example of Building a Layered Curriculum® Unit when C layer requires a great deal of direct instruction.

Some subjects (like math and Advanced Placement courses) require a lot of direct instruction in the C layer. This type of unit works when you have very tight curriculum requirements, if you are teaching for a specific test or in any other situation where student choice must be limited in the bottom layer.

In these situations, remember that you may have to limit student choice. Don't be afraid to keep your C layer looking like a fairly traditional classroom. In other words, the C layer in an AP class may closely resemble any other AP class in that there is heavy emphasis on lecture, note taking and textbook work.

Here are two such examples.

This AP unit allows little choice in the C layer. The heavy curriculum requires a lot of direct instruction and lecture.

AP Biology: Animal Unit : Fish Amphibians & Reptiles
200 pts.

C layer: NO MORE THAN 70 POINTS IN SECTION I (* are required)

*_____1. Lecture Notes 5 pts/day 1 2 3 4 5

*_____2. Vocabulary: Agnatha, Chondrichthyes, Osteichthyes Amphibian, Reptile & the 4 Orders of Reptiles. List main characteristics and improvements. 15 pts

*_____3. Book work assignment: pg. 568__#1-8____10 pts

*_____4. Book work assignment: pg__581_#_4-12 10 pts

Choose One:

_____5. Video: Realm of the Alligator. Write 10 facts and 5 questions generated. 15 pts.

_____6. Choose an amphibian Order. Write a 1 page report on the order using at least two sources. 10 pts.

_____**II. Lab:** 15 pts. Choose ONE ONLY

1. Does a 1 degree (C) water temperature change affect fish respiration?
2. Does caffeine affect fish respiration?

_____III. Library Research. Choose ONE topic. Find 2 articles on the topic. Cite the article. Summarize each article (1/2 page each) then write ½ page of your opinion on the topic. 15 pts.

1. What kinds of environmental issues are affecting amphibians and why.
2. What kinds of environmental issues are affecting the fishing industry.
3. What evidence supports the theory that snakes are lizards without legs

_____EXAM: You will have a 100 point exam on this unit

Most math units need a lot of direct instruction and many math teachers are hesitant to use Layered Curriculum® for that reason. Here's an example of a very traditional high school algebra unit converted into a "daily method" Layered Curriculum® unit.

Exponential and Logarithmic Relations

Assignments with an * are required each day, then choose ONE more from the remaining assignments. Homework is strongly recommended. Homework grades however are based on the spot quizzes at the bell each day. Whenever we have extra class time, please start / continue work on Day 7 activities.

Day 1: Exponential Functions (p 523- 530) (20 points)
*1. Listen / participate in lesson on Graphing exponential functions & Solving exponential equations & inequalities.
2. Small group activity(3 students) work these text problems: 1, 2(a, b, c, d), 3, and 3 more from 4 – 20. Check against answer key. Group discuss errors. Turn in group work.
3. Individual work: work 7 of the book problems from #2 above. Self-check against answer key. Highlight wrong problems. Turn in.
4. Using the link on the board, work through the computer program and email me your work at the end of the class period.

HW: Pg. 528. Work 10 – 15 sample problems of your choice from # 21-55. Choose several from areas you struggled with today. Read over section 10.2 for discussion tomorrow. Be able to demonstrate, identify or define the following terms: exponential function, exponential growth, exponential decay, exponential equation, exponential inequality.

Day 2: Logarithms and Logarithmic Functions *(pp. 531- 538) (20 points)*
*1. Listen / participate in lesson on Evaluating logarithmic expressions & solving logarithmic equations and inequalities.
2. Small group activity(3 students) work these text section problems: 1 - 20 (odd). Check against answer key. Group discuss errors. Turn in group work.
3. Individual work: work 7 of the book problems from #2 above. Self-check against answer key. Highlight wrong problems. Turn in.

*4. Take the homework quiz over last night's homework. 10 points.

HW: Pg. 536. Work 10 – 15 sample problems of your choice from # 21-67. Choose several from areas you struggled with today. Read over section 10.3 for discussion tomorrow. Be able to demonstrate, identify or define the following terms: Logarithm, logarithmic function, logarithmic equation, logarithmic inequality

(Continued)

Day 3: Properties of Logarithms. *(pp. 541-546)* (20 points)
*1. Listen / participate in lesson on Simplifying and Evaluating expressions w/ logarithms & Solving logarithmic equations using the properties of Logarithms.

2. Small group activity(3 students) work these text section problems: 1-12. Check against answer key. Group discuss errors. Turn in group work.
3. Individual work: work 5 of the book problems from #2 above. Self-check against answer key. Highlight wrong problems. Turn in.

*4. Take the homework quiz over last night's homework.   10 points.

HW: Pg. 544. Work 10 – 15 sample problems of your choice from # 13–33 or 38, 39 40.   Choose several from areas you struggled with today. Read over section 10.4 for discussion tomorrow.

Day 4: Common Logarithms *(pp. 547-551) (20 points)*

*1. Listen / participate in lesson on Solving exponential equations and inequalities using common logarithms & Evaluating logarithmic expressions using the Change of Base Formula..
2. Small group activity(3 students) work these text section problems: 1-16. Check against answer key. Group discuss errors. Turn in group work.
3. Individual work: work 5 of the book problems from #2 above. Self-check against answer key. Highlight wrong problems. Turn in.
**4. Take the homework quiz over last night's homework.   10 points.

HW: Pg. 549. Work 10 – 15 sample problems of your choice from # 17-51. Choose several from areas you struggled with today. Read over section 10.5 for discussion tomorrow. Be able to demonstrate, identify or define the following terms: common logarithm, Change of Base Formula.

Day 5: Base e and Natural Logarithms (pp. 554-559) (20 points)
*1. Listen / participate in lesson onEvaluating expressions involving the natural base and natural logarithms & Solving exponential equations and inequalities using natural logarithms.
2. Small group activity(3 students) work these text section problems: 1-19. Check against answer key. Group discuss errors. Turn in group work.
3. Individual work: work 5 of the book problems from #2 above. Self-check against answer key. Highlight wrong problems. Turn in.
**4. Take the homework quiz over last night's homework.   10 points.

HW: Pg. 559. Work 10 – 15 sample problems of your choice from # 21-53 (odd only), 54-59 (all). Choose several from areas you struggled with today. Read over section 10.6 for discussion tomorrow. Be able to demonstrate, identify or define the following terms: natural base, e natural base, exponential, natural logarithm, natural logarithmic function.

(Continued)

Day 6: Exponential Growth and Decay. (pp. 560-565) (20 points)
*1. Listen / participate in lesson on Using logarithms to solve problems involving exponential decay & using logarithms to solve problems involving exponential growth.
2. Small group activity(3 students) work these text section problems: 1-9. Check against answer key. Group discuss errors. Turn in group work.
3. Individual work: work 5 of the book problems from #2 above. Self-check against answer key. Highlight wrong problems. Turn in.
**4. Take the homework quiz over last night's homework.   10 points.
HW: Pg. 565. Work 10 – 15 sample problems of your choice from Pg. 563 #11, 13, 15-18, 23-30   Choose several from areas you struggled with today. Be able to demonstrate, identify or define the following terms: rate of decay, rate of growth .

******Day 7 ***** (Start these any time!! We'll wrap them up on Day 7) (30 points)

B. Layer: Choose any 2 of the following:

1. Make daily observations on any 3 of the bacteria plates in the "lab corner" (do NOT open or shake the plates). Graph the colony growth for a 7 day period. Is the growth exponential? Explain your observations and graph.

2. Do the Graphing Calculator Investigation, pp. 539-540.

3. Do the Graphing Calculator Investigation, pp. 552-553.

HW: * Check for understanding with the Study Guide Review Sheet

*******Day 8 *******REVIEW DAY (10 points)
Grade your review sheet against the key. Buddy up with a classmate to fix your errors.
Take the practice test.
HW: Grade your practice test using the online key.

(Continued)

******Day 9 ***** (25 points)
A Layer: Choose one of the following topics. Find 2 or 3 pieces of research using the internet. Summarize your research (see grading rubric for grammar, format expectations). Write a one paragraph opinion.

1. Examine the rate of growth for the AIDS epidemic in Africa. How does that compare to the rate of growth of the disease
on other continents? Does the rate of growth appear to be slowing? What factors would be involved in slowing the growth rate?

2. From 1967 - 2006 the population in th US has grown by about one-third. Compare the rate of growth for food and wool production duirng the same time period. Project the rates of all these factors into the next half century. Do we need to be concerned?

3. Discuss the pros and cons of China's attempt to slow their population growth rate. Has it been successful?

4. Show a graph of the US government's deficit spending during the Bush presidency. How much of this is related to the war effort? What other major expenses have contributed to the deficit? Is this a good government policy?

5. Global warming: Exponential growth? What other environmental issues can best be explained using logarithms. Describe the event and make an argument that their growth or demise has been "exponential".

******Day 10 ***** (75 points)
TEST DAY

Example of Building a Layered Curriculum ® Unit for early elementary grades.

The most obvious modification for early grades (K-1) is that the unit is written for the teacher's benefit only - it's not normally distributed in a written form to the students. However, the basic ideas remain the same. You want to give the students an opportunity to 1) gather information; 2) manipulate that information; 3) consider some analysis of a debatable topic.

Here is an example of constructing a kindergarten unit:

My Unit Topic will be:
Winter (weather, animals, geography)

My Unit will last:
3 days

Building the C layer:

Key Daily Topics for this Unit:

day 1. Winter Weather
day 2. Winter Animals/habitats/adaptation
day 3. Geographic regions of cold

day 1 Topic: *Winter Weather*
1. Read "Snowy Day" (whole class)
2. Play with "snow" made in blender.
3. Letter sounds - sounds of cold rrrrr, ooooo, aaaaa
4. Picture books of winter (SSR)

day 2 Topic: *Winter Animals/habitats/adaptation*
1. Read "the mitten" (whole class)
2. Sort animal pictures - warm climate/cold climate
3. Draw one winter animal in habitat
4. Build w/clay, animal house for winter.

day 3 Topic: *Geographic regions of cold winter/warm winters*
1. Read "Winter at my House". (whole class)
2. Color world maps - blue/red/yellow zones.

Layered Curriculum® Workbook ©2007

Building the B layer

> 1. How can we tell warm/cold?
> (Students will measure temperature of various water – look at mercury level)
> 2. Will the ice cube melt faster on the window sill, on teacher's desk, outside? (Make a prediction, conduct the lab)

Building the A layer

> What material would make the warmest coat?
> (Students work in small group to analyze various fabrics)

Notes:

Again, Layered Curriculum® units for non-reading grades, such as kindergarten, are usually not handed to the student in a written unit form. The design is written for the benefit of the teacher.

Although C, B, and A grades are also not usually done at this grade level, notice that the layers of thinking complexity are still present. The unit emphasizes new skills and new information then adds some problem solving labs and a critical analysis component.

In this unit, much of the work will be done as whole class instruction, followed by small centers of choice for the students.

Day One: Teacher reads the story and discusses with the class a general overview of the unit they are beginning. Have the students make noises they would make when cold. Show them the letters that make those sounds. Students are then free to move between 3 centers - a play area of snow/slush, an area of picture books related to winter (where the teacher may want to visit with the children to discuss the pictures), and an area where students can practice making some letters which represent sounds made when people or animals are cold.

Day Two: Teacher reads the story followed by a brief discussion of animals and their winter habitats and colors. Students then are free to move between 3 centers (teacher may require time at all 3, choose 2, or let the children decide). This might be a good day to introduce the labs. Teacher can start by showing children how to "read" the red mark on a thermometer and that lower marks mean colder.
Although the teacher may want to "require" the thermometer lab, it may be presented as an option in that children can do it on day 2 or on day 3. The ice cube lab may be done as a "whole class" project, or not.

Day Three: Teacher reads the story. The map assignment may be started as a whole class project, then as students finish they can form groups for the *A layer* activity. The student's analysis would be presented one-on-one with the teacher.

Points could be added to the unit if it fits with a school's needs. Generally, it is just asked of the students to completed "x" number of assignments in the time allowed.

Assigning Points and Grading

The examples on the previous pages include the possible points earned from each assignment. Assigning points to assignments is an area that can take quite a few revisions. In the beginning, work just to get a starting point.

We'll do this by taking the total points of the unit and dividing by the days and minutes of class time.

1. How many points will the entire unit be worth?

my unit will be worth 100 points.

2. Divide the points by the number of days the unit will last.

The unit will last 5 days and will be worth 100 points, then students need to aim for approximately 20 points/day.

Now I have a ratio: **2 min/1 point.**

3. Divide the number of points/day by the number of minutes in your teaching period.

my class period lasts 40 minutes, then each 2 minutes of class time equals 1 point.

This gives you a starting place for assigning points to the various assignments. If I know the video assignment will take about 20 minutes, it will be worth 10 points. If I lecture to the class for 10 minutes, that is worth 5 points, etc.

1. How many points will the entire unit be worth?

2. Divide the points by the number of days the unit will last.

3. Divide the number of points/day by the number of minutes in your teaching period.

This is not a perfect system, and you will need to revise it, but this gives you a starting point for your first unit. Most teachers know approximately how long an assignment will take an average student. For now, we'll use this primitive estimate for assigning points. You will have an opportunity to go back and revise it later.

Designing your point scheme and dividing points between the layers

After you determine which layer (C, B, or A) will require the most emphasis you can assign a proportion to each layer.

For example, in a "bottom heavy" unit, you may want 65/100 points allocated to C layer work, 20/100 points for the B layer and 15/100 for the A layer. In a "middle heavy" unit, you may want 25/100 points for the C layer, 50/100 for the B layer and 25/100 for the A layer. Every teacher's grading scale may be a bit different as their subject and curriculum needs vary.

This allows you to plan an estimated number of assignments of a certain point value to each layer. Obviously you will need to adjust the points as you design assignments. Some assignments may be worth additional points and thus students would do fewer. In other words, if you plan 6 assignments worth 10 points each, you may have some students completing just 3 assignments worth 20 points if those assignments are more difficult.

If you are requiring a formal exam at the end of the unit, don't forget to factor that into your point scheme.

Example for a Project Based Unit:

My unit is worth **100** points.

My C layer will be worth: **25** points
I expect students to do approximately **5** assignments for **5** points each.

My B layer will be worth 50 points
I expect students to do ____ **one** ____ for ____ **50** ____ points each.

My A layer will be worth 25 points
I expect students to do ____ **one** ____ for ____ **25** ____ points each.

Example for a Math Unit:

My unit is worth **150** points.

My C layer will be worth: **60** points
I expect students to do approximately **10** assignments for **6** points each.

My B layer will be worth 24 points
I expect students to do ____ **two** ____ for ____ **12** ____ points each.

My A layer will be worth **16** points
I expect students to do ____ **one** ____ for ____ **16** ____ points each.

A formal exam at the end will be worth ____ **50** ____ points.

An example from high school biology:

My unit is worth *100* points.

My C layer will be worth: *70* points
I expect students to do approximately *7* assignments for *10* points each.

My B layer will be worth *15* points
I expect students to do _**one lab**_ for _15_ points each.

My A layer will be worth *20* points
I expect students to do _**one**_ for _20_ points each.

An example for a "high critical thinking" classroom:

My unit is worth *150* points.

My C layer (review material) will be worth: *20* points
I expect students to do approximately *2* assignments for *10* points each.

My B layer will be worth *40* points
I expect students to do _**two**_ for _20_ points each.

My A layer will be worth *40* points
I expect students to do _**one**_ for _40_ points each.

A formal exam at the end will be worth _____*50*_____ points.

Designing your point scheme.

My unit is worth _____ points.

My C layer will be worth: _____ points

I expect students to do approximately _____ assignments for _____ points each.

My B layer will be worth _____ points

I expect students to do _____ for _____ points each.

My A layer will be worth _____ points.

I expect students to do _____ for _____ points each.

There will / will not be a test at the end worth _____ points,

You may now want to go back to the various layer assignments you designed for your unit and assign a point value to each assignment based on the ratio you established above.

Building Rubrics

The key to making Layered Curriculum® run smoothly is in taking the time to build a rubric or grading criteria for the types of assignments you will be using. At first glance, this may seem an overwhelming task, but if you build rubrics for general types of assignments, you will find that you can use one set of rubrics for most all of your units.

There are many types of grading rubrics and you may have a format that already works for you. Rubrics can range from simple to complex and may need frequent revisions as you see areas for clarification.

We will start here with two examples of a rubric - one simple, one more elaborate.

Example of a simple rubric:

The computer program is worth 10 points. You need to work it for at least a half hour. Complete the self-test at the end. I will ask you 5 of those questions and you will get 2 points for each correct answer.

Example of a more complex rubric:

The Video is worth up to 15 points.

15 points: You watched the entire video, uninterrupted by other activities. Notes were taken representing the entire video. You are able to explain 5-7 ideas learned from the video and can answer 2 out of 3 questions regarding it.

10 points: You watched the entire video, uninterrupted by other activities. Notes may be sketchy. You can explain 3 or 4 ideas learned and can answer some (less than 2/3) of the questions I ask you.

5 points: You watched at least 50% of the video (you may have been distracted by other activities). You can explain 3 or 4 ideas learned but cannot answer more than one question regarding the video.

Notice these rubrics try to clearly point out the expectations of the assignment. They also attempt to show students what types of things might cause them to not earn full credit (such as working on other materials during the video). It helps clarify issues if you will point out both ends of the spectrum to students. In other words, don't just describe what an excellent project looks like, explain what a less than excellent project looks like too. This way the student can see where their work fits.

Choose ONE *C layer* assignment from your unit. Design a Rubric for it.

```
Assignment Type:_____
 (video, book work, flashcards, etc)
Points Possible:_____
Simple Rubric:
```

Share your first rubric with a colleague. Is it clear? Can they see areas which may cause confusion? Revise as needed. Follow this same format for several of your *C layer* assignments. Remember - rubrics need constant revision. Don't be discouraged if you have to revise several times after you've used them with real students!

Examples:

Assignment Type: *Vocabulary Flash cards*

Points Possible: *10*

Simple Rubric: *Using 3 x 5 cards or paper, write the vocabulary word on the front and a simple definition on the back. I will pull 5 cards out of your stack and you will get 2 points for each word you know. The definitions must be in your own words (not copied out of the glossary).*

Assignment Type: *Bookwork (end of chapter questions)*

Points Possible: *15*

Simple Rubric: *Read the chapter and be prepared to answer any of the end-of-the-chapter questions. I will choose 3 questions at random and you will be awarded up to 5 points for each answer. Note 3-4 points awarded for your answer and the additional 1 point for each comes from your ability to elaborate on my follow-up remarks.*

Assignment Type:_____

Points Possible:_____

Simple Rubric:

Assignment Type:_____

Points Possible:_____

Simple Rubric:

Assignment Type:_____
Points Possible:_____
Simple Rubric:

Assignment Type:_____
Points Possible:_____
Simple Rubric:

Assignment Type:_____

Points Possible:_____

Simple Rubric:

Assignment Type:_____

Points Possible:_____

Simple Rubric:

Assignment Type:_____
Points Possible:_____
Simple Rubric:

Assignment Type:_____
Points Possible:_____
Simple Rubric:

Design Rubrics for your B and A layer activities.

A and B layer assignments may have more complex rubrics. Rather than just content, you may be looking for issues here such as grammar, spelling, writing skills, problem solving skills, ability to articulate an opinion, ability to mix fact with personal beliefs, etc. Ask colleagues and your students for input on what should be valued in B and A layer assignments.

Here is an example of a simple *A layer* assignment rubric:

20 points possible. Use an "A Layer" assignment sheet.

Choose one of the A layer questions. Using the library or Internet, find 3 newspaper, magazine or journal articles on your chosen issue. (They need to be less than 5 years old). Read the article. Cite it according to the example in your planner. Write a 3 -5 sentence summary <u>IN YOUR OWN</u> words. On the back of the sheet write 2 good paragraphs (5-7 sentences) of your opinion. Your back opinion must reflect some type of compare/contrast to the articles.

    Points:
- citation correct - 1 pt/each
- Adequate article summary - 2 pts/each - no points if summary is not in your own words.
- Opinion section - 1 point for each good paragraph
- 1 point for each author's opinion you mention in your reflection.
- 1 point for fewer than 6 misspelled words.
- 1 point for fewer than 2 misspelled words.
- 1 point for fewer than 6 grammatical errors.
- 1 point for fewer than 2 grammatical errors.
- 1 point for each supporting argument (up to 2).

Design a Rubric for at least one type of *B layer* application/project:

Assignment Type:
Possible Points:
Rubric:

Design a rubric for your *A Layer* Assignments

Points possible:
Rubric:

Establishing a Grade Scale

What do you expect your students to complete and know in order to earn a *C* grade in your class? This is a question ALL teachers should ask themselves, yet few ever do.

Grade scales vary widely. Sometimes they are decided on by the teacher and sometimes they are handed to us by our school or district. Regardless of what scale you use, you need to structure the points in your unit to meet **your expectations** for the students in your class.

For example, we will begin with one of the simplest grade scales - the 100 point unit.

If my unit is worth 100 points and lasts 5 days: I may want the students to work for about 3 days on *C layer* activities, about 1 day on the *B layer* and 1 day on an *A layer*. So I allocate about 60 points for the *C layer*, and 20 for each of the other 2 layers.

However, I want students to get at least half the points on the B assignment in order to get a B. (I would feel uncomfortable with a student earning a B if his/her *B layer* activity had only earned 1 point!) So I put the cut-off for a "B" half way between 60 and 80. I have similar expectations for the *A layer* too. So, here's my grade scale:

0-40 = F   41-55 = D   56-70 =C   71-85 = B   86+ =A

It's a rather arbitrary scale, but it has worked for me for years. The work students need to do to pass into the next layer meet **my personal expectations** for my course. A student who comes every day, listens to my lecture and takes notes and completes and learns from about 3 other assignments will earn a C. This is my personal expectation.

If my district handed me a grade scale with different numbers, I would have no problem making my unit fit. I would just simply have to go back to my unit and re-evaluate how many points assignments were worth. For example, if I had to use a 93-100 range for an A, then my *A layer* assignments would now be worth 7 points rather than 20.

What do you expect students to complete/learn/master in order to earn at least a "C" grade on this unit?

If they did all that, how many points would the student have?_____

That is your "C." You can add +'s and -'s if it suits your needs. You can also define the minimum required for a passing grade (D).

After completing the *C layer*, how many points would you want a student to earn on his/her *B layer* activity in order to earn a B on the unit?

Add that number to the number of points you established for your *C layer*. That is your "B."

After completing the *B layer*, how many points would you want a student to earn on his/her *A layer* activity in order to earn an A on this unit?

Add that number to the number of points you established for your B cut off. That is your minimum "A".

Your Grade Scale for your unit:
_____ = F _____ = D _____ = C _____ = B _____ = A

You may want/need to add +'s and -'s to the scale. Modify as needed, and establish your barest minimum standard (the point between D and F).

Your First Unit is Finished! - type it up.
Don't forget to include a due date and the grade scale.

Setting up a unit with an emphasis on the B layer when you are mandated to a traditional grade scale.

A common problem faced by teachers is how to set up your unit when you want to emphasize the B layer, but your school's mandated grade scale looks rather traditional, such as 90 - 100 = A., 80 - 89 is a B, etc.

Layered Curriculum is flexible enough that you can make it work with any grading scheme. You may have to be creative however with your point system.

For example, in a Woodworking class, where my B layer is my heaviest layer, we can all see the problem this creates. The C layer is worth 79 points but may be completed in one class period (safety demonstrations, learning about wood, etc) while the student may be working for many, many class periods on their 15 point project. From the student's perspective this looks lopsided. But we can help by mixing in some C layer activities each day, adding things like "effort" "observing safety while working" and other side credits into the C layer.

I might use something like this for a grade scheme:

My unit is worth **100** points.

My C layer will be worth: **79** points
I expect students to do approximately **2** assignments for **10** points each and **12** assignments for **5** points each.

My B layer will be worth **15** points
I expect students to do **one** for **15** points each.

My A layer will be worth **10** points
I expect students to do **one** for **10** points each.

Evaluating Your Unit BEFORE Handing It Out

It is extremely helpful to ask a colleague to assist you in this evaluation.

*C layer

Do I have assignments for visual learners?
Do I have assignments for auditory learners?_____
Do I have assignments for tactile learners?
Do I have enough assignments for poor/non-readers?
Do I have enough assignments to stretch my high ability students?
my lowest ability student?_____

Do I have 2 or 3 times as many points offered as points needed. (If
you want students to do 50 points, do you offer at least 100 points in
options?)

*Each layer should accommodate the full spectrum of students in your class.
Try not to exclude any one, but remember every classroom is unique.   If an
issue does NOT fit your particular population, then just write "N/A."

B layer

Double check - are the *B layer* activities asking students to think on
a more complex scale? Are they applying new skills or knowledge
they learned in the *C layer*?

A layer

Did you tie in current issues / debate whenever possible?
Are you asking questions which require factual information gathering
as well as opinion, value judgement, moral reasoning, etc.?

Evaluating Your Layered Curriculum® Unit AFTER It's Over

Now that you've finished your first unit, you probably have learned more than the kids! It is time for revisions.

What general aspects went well? (Timing, rubrics, one-on-one assessment, variety, engaging students, student success?)

What would you like to add?

What do you want to discontinue doing or modify?

If you feel like overall things went well:
Congratulations. You may now want to go back over your unit and make some notes about which assignments were popular, which were not chosen at all, which types students struggled with, etc. This is also a good time to look back over your rubrics and add points of clarification. From there you are ready to design your next unit. Have fun!

If you feel a bit overwhelmed:

That's fine too. It's a common feeling whenever you are trying something new. Here are some self-reflecting questions and suggestions for you.

_____Do you need to add more time?

If very few students were able to actually complete any assignments, you may need to either shorten the assignments, add more time to the unit, or require some things done as homework. Perhaps assignments were more involved than you originally expected. Cut back.

_____Do you need to shorten time?

If too many students were not using time wisely, it could be that you offered too much time for activities. Try decreasing the time, adding a higher number of completed assignments each day, or more structure. You may want one activity due at the end of half the period and another at the end.

_____Do you need fewer activities to occur at one time?

If you felt like a chicken running around without a head, you may need to slow it down. Try starting with only 2 choices of activities going at once. If you get comfortable with that, then you may want to add one more. Different teaching styles and different populations of kids have different tolerances for activity levels. If the oral defense caught you running behind, don't try to talk to every student about every assignment. Try every other one, or let the student choose one thing to discuss with you. Work up to more.

Appendix

C Layer Activity/Assignment Suggestions

traditional book work

flash cards for vocabulary

flash cards for reading (summarize each section on back)

dioramas

puppet shows

debate

design a board game

design a book to teach concept to a younger child

mobile

auditory lesson station

literature circles

a brochure

library reports

annotated Internet bibliography

webpages

power point presentation

poster

bulletin board

collage

model

worksheets

computer programs

debate

book reports

demonstrations

lectures

B Layer Activity Suggestions

Problem Solving Labs

Which is a better cleaner, a base or an acid?
Will saliva dissolve a protein? Lipid? Carbohydrate?
Can you germinate a seed in milk? Coke? Distilled water?
Which player has the best stats?
Graph your Halloween haul
Who spends more time in the bathroom, boys or girls?
Which gum has the longest lasting flavor?
How much t.v does the average student in our class watch?
How many of your shoes would it take to stretch across the school?
Community Service Projects

Application Projects

Apply your writing/typing/grammar skills in another subject
Design a brochure/pamphlet/children's book using your skills
Build
Bake
Perform
Design/Graph
Write a theme using the components learned in the C layer
Display a portfolio using the assignments from the C layer
Prepare a demonstration to teach the skills learned in the C layer
Find examples where history has repeated itself and compare/contrast
Use the vocabulary/letter/math skills learned in C layer to write, build, create
Speak before your school board on this issue
Start and implement a letter writing campaign
Build a website for . . .

<u>ANY</u> Interdisciplinary Assignment

100 A Layer Questions

1 Should we fluoridate our water?

2 Will there be a cure for AIDS in your lifetime?

3 Are pesticides on crops worth the risk?

4 Are steroids safe to use? Ever?

5 Do schools put too much emphasis on sports?

6 Are bio-engineered plants a good idea?

7 Are weight loss aids harmful?

8 Are vegetarians healthier?

9 What is really harming our ozone?

10 Should food additives be avoided?

11 How did the Great Depression influence this year's economic politics?

12 What historical figures could you compare to Bill Gates?

13 Is the Harry Potter Movie better than the book?

14 If Martin Luther King Jr. had never lived, would someone else have played that role?

15 Should 16 year olds be allowed to drive? Should 86 year olds?

16 In what ways would our town be different if the Confederacy had won the war?

17 Why do we not have a WWII memorial?

18 Did the US know of the Pearl Harbor attack before it happened?

19 Who killed JFK?

20 What is the most efficient table/chair arrangement in this classroom?

21 How long should our class periods last?

22 Who was responsible for the deaths of Romeo and Juliet?

23 What happened to Amelia Earhart?

24 Would you sail through the Bermuda Triangle?

25 From Greeks to Modern Wave Theory, how has the scientific view of the nature of matter changed?

26 Is the government responsible for keeping our food safe?

27 Who should win the World Series this year?

28 Who is the best athlete in our school?

29 Is t.v. good or bad?

30 How much television should children watch?

31 What is a good bedtime for the students in this classroom?

32 Do third graders get enough exercise?

33 Does our school cafeteria provide a balanced lunch?

34 Is it safe to fly?

35 Who is the best Opera singer alive today?

36 Who is the best singer alive today?

37 Should we have Channel One time?

38 Is our playground equipment safe?

39 Which story was better?

40 Why was the Grinch so "grinchy"?

41 What makes people mean?

42 Is there life on other planets?

43 Is the NASA space program worth what we spend on it?

44 What is the best commercial on television?

45 Do we need police in our schools?

46 Did we really learn anything from the Holocaust?

47 What happened to the dinosaurs?

48 Where is the best place to sit in the auditorium?

49 What is the best rollercoaster?

50 Where did that anthrax come from?

51 Does our government spend more money on foreign aid to "white countries" than countries of dark-skinned populations?

52 What were the most important events in the civil-rights movement?

53 If Martin Luther King were alive today, what would please him the most? Least?

Least?

54 What most influenced the Declaration of Independence?

55 What countries/nationalities have most influenced America's food?

56 Which country, outside of the US, has the best holidays?

57 Which fonts are the best to use on billboards? Pamphlets? Print ads?

58 Which performance of "The Nutcracker" was better?

59 What most influences a person's drug use/ non-use?

60 Which character was the best "friend?"

61 Who wrote Shakespeare?

62 What should go in Thanksgiving stuffing?

63 Which of these fabrics would make the warmest coat?

64 Who is the stronger candidate?

65 Did our city benefit from the Olympics?

66 How much of our class budget should we spend on field trips?

67 Which animal makes the best class pet?

68 Should school busses have seat belts?

69 Are there any safe recreational drugs?

70 Which room has the best use of color?

71 Are we prepared for an earthquake?

72 Which instrument sounds most like a fox?

73 What would be today's version of a mountain man?

74 Which character changed the most in the story?

75 Is there a better way to design a keyboard?

76 Is it safe to drink raw milk?

77 In order, who is to blame for the destruction by hurricane Katrina?

78 Will instant messaging change our status quo on grammar and spelling?

79 Does the government need to be involved in animal identification?

80 Corn has now become part of the bio-fuel industry. What is the effect on farming?

83 Is a killer asteroid heading our way?

84 What architect made the most significant contribution to 20th century development?

85 Why do people love or hate opera?

86 Is it right that everyone in the school cafeteria gets the same sized portion?

87 How could Bach have physically written the volumes he did? Did he have help from other members of his family?

88 Why do schools still have traditional bands when they haven't been popular in mainstream culture in over 100 years?

89 Is Hip-Hop really music?

90 Which is better, stick-built or modular built?

91 Should a cabinet maker in the US be paid more than a cabinet maker in China?

92 Is a college education worth the cost?

93 What do IQ tests really measure?

94 Which makes a better queen bee, a Carniolan or a Russian?

95 Why might organic food be better for you?

96 What would your ideal weight be? Your healthiest?

97 How and when should cell phones be used in school?

98 Should principals teach classes?

99 What time should our school day begin?

100 Why do we need to travel in space?

A Layer Assignment Sheet

Name_____ Unit # or title_____

Topic #_____

Summarize 3 recent magazine, journal, Internet articles on your topic. On the back of this sheet write 2 good paragraphs (5 - 7 sentences make a good paragraph) on your opinion. Make sure to mention some of the research in your opinion. You will be graded on spelling, punctuation and grammar in addition to the quality of your summaries (see grading rubric for further information).

1. Title of Article:
Title of Magazine or Journal or URL:
Author:
Date of Article:
Summary:

2. Title of Article:
Title of Magazine or Journal or URL:
Author:
Date of Article:
Summary:

3. Title of Article:
Title of Magazine or Journal or URL:
Author:
Date of Article:
Summary:

FAQs
(See the text for more frequently asked questions)

How can I tell if an assignment belongs in the *C* or *B layer*?

Generally, *C layer* activities are ones which involve basic skills and knowledge. Things in here include rote memorization, finding answers to questions, reports, and such.
B layer activities generally are assignments which involve an application of the material learned in the *C layer*.
However, there really is no hard and fast rule. Sometimes you may decide to put an application type activity in the *C layer* just because it is a rather simple project. You may want to save *B layer* activities for more complex projects.

What about Homework?

Views and policies on homework vary widely among teachers and schools. Here again, go with what fits your comfort level and/or your school's requirements. Some teachers specifically assign certain activities to be done as homework. Some teachers put an asterisk(*) by assignment choices that must be done at home. Some teachers leave the *A layer* assignments for homework. And some teachers do not assign homework, per se. They just leave it up to individual students as to whether or not they need to take some of their assignments home to complete.

How much can be done as "whole class instruction?"

I think the popularity of Layered Curriculum partly comes from the fact that it is so very flexible and easy to modify for your personal teaching style, grade level, or school requirement. It is quite easy to modify the grading scale, frequency of testing, homework, and the amount of whole class instruction needed.
If a teacher feels that the entire *C layer* is best presented in a traditional whole class discussion/lecture approach, then fine. Perhaps the student choice can be added at the *B layer* and *A layer*. Don't be afraid to do some direct instruction. Sometimes that is what is needed.

One of the things I strongly suggest to teachers is to go slow. You don't have to jump in up to your neck on the first unit. Start with what you are currently doing and are comfortable with. Then look for how you can modify that a little. Perhaps you just want to start by adding an application project, or maybe just an *A layer*, critical analysis piece.
If lots of activities going on overwhelm you, then start with two. Once you are comfortable with that, you may want to add a third, and so on.

Layered Curriculum® Lesson Planner

Unit topic: _____Start Date_____Finish Date_____

C Layer Objectives	Assignment	points
(Day 1 or) Objective 1:	1. 2. 3. 4.	
Objective 2:	1. 2. 3. 4.	
Objective 3:	1. 2. 3. 4.	
Objective 4:	1. 2. 3. 4.	
Objective 5	1. 2. 3. 4.	

B Layer objective(s)	Assignment	Points
	1.	
	2.	
	3.	

A Layer	(Essential Questions, Current Event, Debatable Real World Topic)	points
	1.	
	2.	
	3.	

Assessments:

Materials to gather:

Things to copy:

Notes

Notes

Layered Curriculum® Workbook ©2007

Notes